RAIN FORESTS

Contents

Introduction

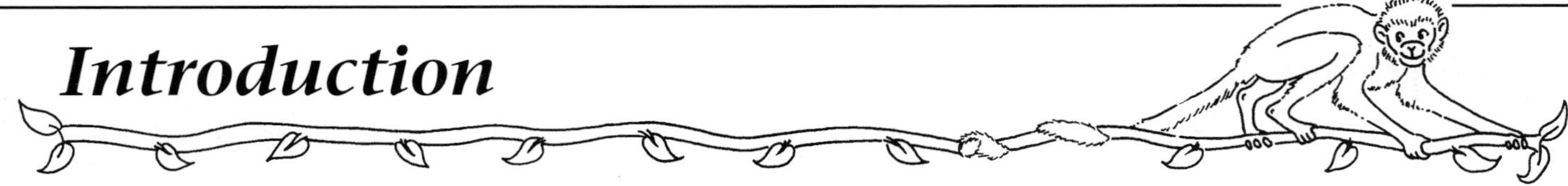

THE RAIN FOREST TOPIC
Rain forests are found in both tropical and temperate parts of the world. They contain thousands of varieties of animals, birds, insects and plants. They are rich in resources – many of the things that we eat and drink come from these regions of the world and some of the medicines we use were developed from rainforest plants. Today, large areas of forest are being chopped down for timber or burnt as fuel, or cleared to make way for new roads, ranches and homes. Many of the plants and creatures of the forest are now endangered because of hunters, loggers, developers and mining operations, and in some cases risk complete extinction in the next few years. Losing vast areas of rain forest will also affect the world's climate.

USING THE WORKSHEETS
This pack of rainforest worksheets has been designed as a flexible resource for use in the primary classroom. The sheets can be used as starting points to spark discussion and stimulate new ideas, or to enhance and develop skills on work in progress.

The pack has been arranged in broad themes for ease of use:

Sheets 1–5:	What is a rain forest? This section serves as an introduction to the topic, looking at the basic characteristics, location and climate of rain forests.
Sheets 6–10:	Plant life
Sheets 11–19:	Animal life
Sheets 20–24:	People in the rain forest, and environmental issues.
Sheet 25:	A glossary for pupils to complete as they work through the sheets.

Within each theme, the sheets become progressively more demanding, so there are worksheets dealing with, for example, animal life, to suit children of varying abilities. However, many of the ideas can easily be adapted for less able children.

The majority of the sheets are designed to be used by children working on their own, although several are designed for pupils working in small groups.

Most of the sheets can be completed without any need for further reference, apart from an atlas or dictionary. New vocabulary is introduced and children will have the opportunity to use this in other parts of the pack. The vocabulary used relates to the rainforest topic. Contextual clues should provide children with enough information to help them with unfamiliar words and phrases. It is assumed that they will have access to other support material provided by the teacher.

All the material has been produced in line with the National Curriculum. Several worksheets focus on literacy and numeracy while others look at scientific, geographical and environmental issues. This is made clear in the support and extension notes and summarised in the topic web opposite.

It should also be possible to adapt and develop the sheets for your own school's needs. They have been designed to give children a chance to demonstrate their knowledge and understanding about a subject and to explore further.

TOPIC WEB
This shows how the different worksheets and follow-up activities link into specific curriculum areas.

SUPPORT AND EXTENSION NOTES
Each sheet is an individual resource and most require little more than a pencil and crayons to complete. The support and extension notes detail the learning outcomes, teaching points, answers to questions, and offer ideas for follow-up activities.

FURTHER INFORMATION
A list of further resources, including information books, a tape, a CD-ROM, useful addresses and places to visit, is provided on page 7.

Topic Web

This topic web shows how the worksheets and follow-up activities link into specific curriculum areas. Figures in brackets refer to the numbers of the worksheets.

Rain Forests

ENGLISH
- comprehension (1) (3) (5) (7) (8) (13) (15) (16) (19) (20) (21) (23)
- cloze procedure (1) (6) (13) (16)
- reasoning skills (3) (5) (6) (16) (19) (22)
- research skills (1) (2) (6) (7) (8) (9) (10) (14) (16)
- following instructions (9) (12) (21) (22)
- sequencing instructions (5) (9)
- using adjectives (14)
- descriptive writing (8) (14) (18) (20)
- reading / writing poetry (14)
- story writing (11) (18)
- play writing (18)
- letter writing (4) (19) (20) (24)
- writing a recipe (9)
- writing a diary (20)
- lists (10) (14) (22)
- layout and presentation (4) (9) (17) (19) (23) (24)
- putting points of view (19) (24)
- group discussion (1) (2) (4) (5) (8) (9) (10) (12) (14) (16) (17) (18) (19) (20) (21) (22) (23) (24)
- using glossaries (5) (7) (8) (13) (14) (16) (17) (19) (25)

MATHEMATICS
- handling data (3) (4)
- using diagrams and graphs (3) (4)
- measuring skills (3) (4)
- mapping skills:
  using grids and co-ordinates, using scales, deciphering and using symbols (3)
- mazes (11)
- symmetry (12)
- board games (21)

SCIENCE
- water cycle / evaporation (5)
- plant life (1) (5) (6) (7) (8) (9) (10) (17) (23) (24)
- growing plants (5) (9)
- transpiration (5)
- plant / nutrient cycle (8)
- decomposition (8)
- photosynthesis (17)
- animal life (1) (6) (8) (11) (12) (13) (14) (15) (16) (17) (18) (19) (23)
- variation and classification (11) (13) (14) (16) (19)
- animal adaptation (6) (12) (13) (15) (16) (19)
- food chains and webs (17)
- food hygiene (9)
- classifying materials (10)

IT
- use of Internet (4)

MUSIC / DRAMA
- composing / performing (18)
- listening / appraising (18)
- using percussion, electronic keyboard (18)

GEOGRAPHY
- using an atlas (1) (2) (3) (7) (11) (16)
- mapping skills (3)
- studying localities (1) (2) (3) (4) (7) (14) (20)
- weather and climate (1) (2) (4) (5) (7) (23)
- the seasons (4) (7)
- water cycle (5)
- rivers (1) (5) (14)
- resources (1) (9) (10) (20) (23)
- human geography (10) (19) (20) (23)
- environmental issues (19) (23) (24)

D & T
- following instructions (9)
- designing and making skills:
  rain gauge (4)
  collage (6) (10)
  recipe card (9)
  mobile (12) (17)
  bird table (15)
  posters (19) (23)
  game (21)
  spinner (21)

ART
- drawing (3) (4) (11) (12) (13) (17) (18) (19) (23)
- use of colour (6) (9) (12) (18) (19) (23)
- designing and making (3) (6) (9) (10) (12) (17) (19) (21) (23)
- collage (6) (10)
- symmetrical patterns (12)
- illustrating:
  recipe (9)
  cartoon strip (11)
  story (18)
  posters (19) (23)

Support and extension notes

1. What is a Rain Forest?
Learning outcome: Comprehension of basic rainforest facts. (Geography, Science, English)
Teaching points: Use in conjunction with Sheet 2 and an atlas; point out where the Equator is and where most rain forests are found. Explain why rain forests are so rich in animal and plant life, and how forests affect the climate. Look at books containing photographs of rain forests.
Answers: 1. Equator, 2. wet, 3. tall, 4. close together, 5. dark, 6. warm and damp, 7. plants and animals, 8. Amazon rain forest in South America, 9. (as final paragraph).
Follow-up activities:
• In small groups, use information books to find out more about the Amazon rain forest and Amazon River.
• Study a local patch of woodland. Produce a set of questions with a set of multiple choice answers.

2. Where are the Rain Forests?
Learning outcomes: To locate the world's main areas of tropical and temperate rain forest. To find out how to use the contents page and index of an atlas and identify the Equator, and the Tropics of Cancer and Capricorn. (Geography, English)
Teaching points: Use an atlas and a globe as well as the map provided. Explain how to use an atlas. Explain that there are two types of rain forest – tropical and temperate.
Follow-up activities:
• Use an atlas to identify the other countries shaded black. Are the rain forests here likely to be tropical or temperate?
• Are there any rain forests in Europe? Do the children know why this might be? Discuss the differences between where we live and rainforest environments.

3. Tropical Island
Learning outcomes: To improve mapping skills: practise using an atlas, compass points, grids and co-ordinates, keys and symbols, scales. To locate Britain and St Lucia using an atlas. (Geography, Maths, English)
Teaching points: Explain key features of maps and how to use them.
Answers: 1a. South America, 1b. Caribbean Sea, 1c. Windward Islands (Lesser Antilles). 3a. west, 3b. south, 3c. north, 4a. C1, 4b. B3, 4c. A3, 4d. C6, 4e. A3, B2,3,4, C2,3,4, D4.
Follow-up activities:
• Set further tasks related to St Lucia map, e.g. use scale to measure distances, design symbols to denote areas of forest, crops, settlement. Where is most settlement found? Why?
• Look at symbols used on Ordnance Survey and other maps.
• Produce a simple map of the school or your own locality. Draw a grid over it. Mark on the major features. Practise using co-ordinates to find places on the map.

4. What's the Weather Like?
Learning outcomes: To find out about weather conditions in different parts of the world. To understand block graphs and handle data. (Geography, Maths)
Teaching points: Compare the weather/rainfall in St Lucia with that of London. Make a block graph of rainforest rainfall and draw further comparisons. Discuss differences between seasonal and non-seasonal weather patterns.
Answers: 1. Feb/Oct, 2. May/Mar, 3. June/Apr.
Follow-up activities:
• Make a rain gauge and leave it out in the open. Take daily readings for a month. Compare with that of St Lucia.
• Form an Internet or letter link with a school in St Lucia to find out more about the country.

5. The Water Cycle
Learning outcomes: To understand how the water cycle works. To learn that plant growth is affected by the availability of water. (Science)
Teaching points: Explain the water cycle and the meaning of 'evaporation'. Make specific reference to the importance of rain forests and their rivers to the world's climate.
Answers: Col. 1: 6, 2, 5 Col. 2: 3, 1, 4
Follow-up activities:
• Discuss what happens to the water in a puddle when the sun shines. Put a saucer of water on to a sunny window sill and examine it a few days later.
• Explain transpiration. Put a plant into a clear polythene bag and secure the bag around the stem. Put it in a sunny place. Examine it after a day or so. Discuss the results.

6. Rainforest Layers
Learning outcomes: To find out about the different layers of vegetation within a tropical rain forest. To learn that plants and animals are found in different habitats, and are suited to their environment. (Science, English)
Teaching points: Explain that each layer is an ideal habitat for the particular plants and animals that exist within it, and that they are all interdependent.
Answers: 1.emergent trees, 2.canopy, 3.understorey, 4.forest floor. a & d. forest floor, b. canopy, c. emergent trees, e. understorey.
Follow-up activities:
• Use books to find out more about rainforest animals. As a group, make a collage showing which creatures are found in the various layers of the forest.

7. What's the Difference?
Learning outcomes: Comprehension of the differences between temperate and tropical rain forests; evergreen and deciduous trees. (Geography, Science, English)
Teaching points: Refer to sheet 2 and an atlas. Clarify what is meant by 'conifer', 'evergreen', 'deciduous'.
Answers: Tropical: 1, 3, 7, 8, 10; Temperate: 2, 4, 5, 6, 9.
Follow-up activities:
• Compare temperate rain forests with temperate woodland in this country.
• Find out more about temperate rain forests in New Zealand and Australia, and their trees (e.g. New Zealand's kauri pine).

8. Decaying Leaves
Learning outcomes: To understand the meaning of decomposition, and that plants need nutrients as well as water for growth. (Science, English)
Teaching points: Explain the plant cycle. Discuss the seasons, and why decomposition happens continually in tropical forests, but is more seasonal in temperate regions.
Answers: 1. decomposition, 2. tiny creatures, 3. mineral salts, 4. hot and humid, 5. food.

Follow-up activities:
• Set up an experiment to find out how things decay. Bury a plastic bottle, a newspaper and some deciduous leaves. Examine after a week; discuss what has happened and why.
• As a group, visit a local wood in autumn. Which creatures can be found among the decaying leaves? Find out what part they play in the process of decay.

9. Tropical Tastes
Learning outcomes: To understand that rain forests provide food resources and identify some of them. To understand how to write a recipe, the importance of clear instructions, also of food hygiene. (Geography, Science, English, Art)
Teaching points: Discuss where the fruits we eat come from. (Are they all tropical or are any grown near home?) How do they get here? Look at simple recipes: how are they laid out and illustrated? Explain importance of food hygiene.
Answers: 1. bananas, 2. pineapple, 3. mango, 4. lychees, 5. papaya, 6. starfruit, 7. avocado.
Follow-up activities:
• Have a blind tasting session using some of the rainforest fruits that can be bought at a supermarket. Try to match the taste to the fruit.
• Grow plants from the fruit pips, seeds, nuts and stones. Explain what seedlings need to grow healthy and strong.

10. Rainforest Resources
Learning outcome: To find out more about rainforest resources, in particular rubber, and its various uses in our everyday lives. (Geography, Science, English)
Teaching points: Discuss which other products are made from rubber. Investigate some of the other products that come from rainforest regions, e.g. coffee, mahogany.
Answers: all except books and chewing gum; e.g. bicycle wheels, shoe soles, erasers; 1A, 2D, 3B, 4C.
Follow-up activities:
• Make a display of items made from rubber. Investigate some of the properties of rubber.
• Read Antonio's Rainforest, which includes plenty of facts about rubber and describes the life of a rubber tapper's family in the Brazilian rain forest.
• Collect magazine photographs of other rainforest products (e.g. furniture, cosmetics). Make an illustrated class list.

11. Monkey Puzzle
Learning outcomes: Bio-diversity of life: monkeys are found in rain forests, but there are different kinds in different countries. Understanding what is meant by a maze. Using an atlas to identify countries. (Science, Geography, Maths)
Teaching points: Variation within species. Explanation of the word 'maze'. Using an atlas.
Answers: 1. Diana monkey, 2. tamarin, 3. lar gibbon, 4. macaque.
Follow-up activities:
• Further work on mazes.
• Find a selection of stories about monkeys to read aloud, e.g. the Buddhist tale about The Monkey King.
• Monkeys are known to be mischievous. Write a funny story called 'Monkey Trouble' as a cartoon strip.
• Visit a local wildlife park or zoo to see different monkeys.
• What is a 'monkey puzzle'? (Monkey puzzle forests grow in south-east Chile.)

12. Butterfly Patterns
Learning outcomes: To find out about both symmetry and camouflage. (Maths, Science)
Teaching points: Explain symmetry. Show examples. Explain camouflage and show examples from rain forests (e.g. tree frogs, chameleons).
Follow-up activities:
• Try other methods of making symmetrical patterns, such as using a mirror; painting only one half of a butterfly drawing and folding it in half while still wet.
• Cut out the butterfly squares to make a butterfly mobile.
• Arrange a visit to a butterfly farm.
• Develop the camouflage theme: how would children camouflage themselves in various surroundings (e.g. in a wood in autumn, in snow)?

13. What's Down There?
Learning outcomes: To recognize some of the creatures of the forest floor and learn that some prey on others. To complete fact boxes from information provided. (Science, English)
Teaching points: Discuss the meaning of the words 'predator' and 'prey'. Explain that some predators are prey for others.
Answer: leaf-cutting ant.
Follow-up activities:
• Arrange an insect hunt. Identify the insects. Make sure that children handle the insects carefully and return them to their natural surroundings afterwards. Draw some of the creatures found. Look at ways in which these creatures have adapted to their surroundings.

14. River Reptiles
Learning outcomes: To understand the characteristics of reptiles. To become familiar with the function of adjectives. (Science, Geography, English)
Teaching points: Explain the characteristics of reptiles. Elicit other examples. Discuss the function of adjectives. Before attempting the sheet, ask the children to brainstorm which words best describe a crocodile. Explain different types of poetry, with examples (e.g. rhymes, limericks, nonsense verse).
Follow-up activities:
• Find out about other members of the crocodile family. In which of the world's rain forests do they live?
• Find out about other rainforest reptiles and river creatures.
• Find poems about rainforest creatures to read aloud and discuss in class.
• Collect and classify adjectives e.g. for colours, sizes, moods.

15. Birds and Beaks
Learning outcomes: To understand animal adaptation; that birds' beaks have evolved according to their feeding habits. To increase knowledge of rainforest birdlife. (Science, English)
Teaching points: Discuss the importance of a bird's beak to its survival.
Answers: 1. hummingbird, 2. harpy eagle, 3. scarlet macaw, 4. toucan, 5. skimmer.
Follow-up activities:
• Design and make a bird table to set up in the school grounds. Identify the birds. Watch them feed. Notice their beak shapes and what they eat.

16. Rainforest Mammals
Learning outcomes: To understand the characteristics of mammals. To complete fact boxes selecting only relevant text from facts available. (Science, Geography, English)

Teaching points: Explain the characteristics of mammals. Look at photographs of orang-utans and sloths. Use an atlas to find out where they live. Discuss how they have adapted to life in the rain forest.
Follow-up activities:
• Find pictures of other rainforest mammals. Locate where they live. How have they adapted to their environment?
• Which mammals can be found in this country? Are any of them similar to those found in rain forests?

17. Food Chains
Learning outcomes: To understand the meaning of food webs and chains and be able to construct simple examples. To understand the difference between carnivores and herbivores. (Science, English)
Teaching points: Explain that most food chains begin with green plants, which make their own food by photosynthesis (explain photosynthesis), and end with a carnivore. Discuss what happens if one part of the food chain disappears.
Answers: jaguar, macaw, piranha, leaves, bird-eating spider.
Follow-up activities:
• Think of more food chain examples, based in this country.
• As a class, put together a food web, made up of food chains. Make a food web mobile.

18. Rainforest Dreams
Learning outcome: To use knowledge of rainforest plants, animals and weather gained so far to write and illustrate an imaginative story. (English, Geography, Art)
Teaching points: As revision of the topic, elicit information from the class about rain forests. Read out some descriptions of what a rain forest is like. Show photographs or slides to set the mood. Play a cassette of rainforest sounds.
Follow-up activities:
• As a class, create rainforest music/noises using percussion instruments/electronic keyboard.
• Ask children to write a play based on their story. Act out the play to the class, while others play suitable sound effects.

19. Top Cats
Learning outcomes: To find out about endangered rainforest species, why they are at risk, and what is being done to protect them. To understand the difference between 'endangered' and 'extinct'. (Science, English)
Teaching points: This is a comprehension exercise with information supplied in the text, but Q.8 could become a class discussion and Q.9 a group exercise.
Follow-up activities:
• Design and make posters highlighting the plight of tigers.
• Look at the different kinds of cats that live in the forest. Consider how they have adapted to survive in the rain forests. Compare them to domestic cats.

20. Antonio Lives in the Rain Forest
Learning outcome: To find out about people in other countries; to compare a child's way of life in the rain forest with life here. (Geography, English)
Teaching points: As a lead-in to a piece of creative writing, discuss the differences and similarities between life here and life in a rain forest. Would the children like to live in a rain forest? If so why? What would they miss about life here?
Follow-up activities:
• Read Antonio's Rainforest, about a real child in the Amazon rain forest, from which this extract was taken.
• Ask children to write a diary of a typical week in their life.

21. Rainforest Trek - 1
Learning outcome: To introduce the idea of creating games. (Maths, English)
Teaching points: Games are an excellent way for children to learn while they play together.
Follow-up activities:
• Ask children to think of other hazards they might come across in a rain forest.
• Make a six-sided spinner to use instead of a dice.
• In small groups, children could make up their own rainforest game based on a track or grid, similar to the one used for snakes and ladders.

22. Rainforest Trek - 2
Learning outcomes: To develop reasoning skills and experience writing lists. (English)
Teaching points: Discuss the importance of making lists. Who makes lists and why?
Follow-up activities:
• Ask the children to write a list of what they might need if they were going on an expedition up a mountain, or into a desert.

23. Deforestation
Learning outcome: To understand the meaning of deforestation and some of the environmental problems it causes. (Geography, Science, English)
Teaching points: Explain why rain forests are so important, not only to the rainforest peoples and creatures, but to all life on this planet. Explain how destroying huge areas of forest will affect the world's climate.
Answers: true, true, true, false, true.
Follow-up activities:
• Ask children to think of ways they can help save the rain forests (e.g. write to furniture firms and find out what they are doing to stop the use of rainforest hardwoods for furniture).
• Make posters on the theme of saving the rain forests.

24. Down it Comes
Learning outcomes: To develop further understanding of environmental issues. To understand the importance of clarity and brevity in formal written communication. (Geography, English)
Teaching points: Ask children to put themselves in the place of the villagers and discuss their feelings. Look at how the manager's letter has been laid out (address, date, etc.).
Follow-up activities:
• Examine some of the other ways it is possible to put or argue a point of view (e.g. protests, strikes, petitions, leaflets, sponsored walks).
• Ask the children to write a letter protesting about something they object to in the local area or at school.

25. Glossary
Learning outcomes: To become familiar with dictionaries and glossaries. To reinforce vocabulary on the rainforest topic. (English, Geography)
Teaching points: Practise using dictionaries and information books with glossaries.
Follow-up activity:
• Compare glossary entries produced by the class.
• Devise a simple crossword using rainforest words. Ask children to write the clues.
• Develop class glossaries on other topics.

Further information

INFORMATION BOOKS:

The Amazon by Julia Waterlow (Wayland, 1992)
Animals by Habitat: Animals of the Rain Forest by Stephen Savage (Wayland, 1996)
Antonio's Rainforest by Anna Lewington (Wayland, 1992)
Closer Look at the Rain Forest by Selina Wood (Franklin Watts, 1996)
Deep in the Rain Forest series by Saviour Pirotta (Wayland, 1998)
Forests for Life by Edward Parker (Wayland, 1997)
The Landscape of St Lucia by Alison Brownlie (Wayland, 1998)
The Living Forests by Clive Wilson (Kingfisher, 1994)
Look Who Lives In the Rain Forest by Alan Baker (Macdonald Young Books, 1998)
People and Places in Peril: Rainforests by Sara Oldfield (Cherrytree Books, 1995)
The People of St Lucia by Alison Brownlie (Wayland, 1998)
The Wayland Atlas of Rain Forests by Anna Lewington and Edward Parker (Wayland, 1996)
Wide World: People of the Rain Forests by Anna Lewington and Edward Parker (Wayland, 1998)
Wildside on Rain Forests by Paul Appleby (BBC, 1992)
World of the Rain Forest by Rosie McCormick (Franklin Watts, 1997)
Worldwise: Rainforest by Penny Clarke (Franklin Watts, 1996)

USEFUL ADDRESSES:

Flora & Fauna Preservation Society, 79-83 North St, Brighton, Sussex, BN1 1ZA
Friends of the Earth, 26-28 Underwood Street, London N1 7QJ
Living Earth Foundation, 4 Great James Street, London WC1N 3DA
The Rain Forest Foundation, 5 Fitzroy Lodge, The Grove, London N6 5JU
Reforest the Earth, 42-46 Bethel Street, Norwich NR2 1NR
World Wide Fund for Nature, Panda House, Weyside Park, Godalming, Surrey GU7 1XR

AUDIO TAPE:

Environmental Sounds: Tropical Jungle (The Nature Company, Tel: 001 510 644 1337) Recordings from the Amazon, including a rainstorm passing overhead, a jaguar's roar and a spider monkey's chatter.

CD-ROM:

Exploring Land Habitats (Wayland, 1997)

PLACES TO VISIT:

Botanic Gardens, Stranmills Road, Belfast, Northern Ireland
Buckfast Butterflies, Buckfast, Devon TQ11 0DZ
Butterfly and Falconry Park, Long Sutton, Lincolnshire PE12 9LE
Butterfly House, Syon Park, Brentford, Middlesex TW8 8JF
Butterfly World, Queens Park, Chorley New Road, Bolton, Lancashire BL1 4RU
Edinburgh Butterfly & Insect World, Dobbies Garden Centre, Lasswade, Midlothian, Scotland EH18 1AZ
Linton Zoological Gardens, Hadstock Road, Linton, Cambridgeshire
Logan Botanic Garden, Port Logan, Stranraer, Wigtownshire, Scotland DG9 9ND
Manor House Wildlife Park, St Florence, Tenby, Dyfed, Wales SA70 8RJ
Natural History Museum, Cromwell Road, London SW7 5BD
New Forest Nature Quest, Longdown, Ashurst, Hampshire
Newquay Zoo, Trenance Park, Newquay, Cornwall TR7 2LZ
Royal Botanical Gardens, Kew, Richmond, Surrey TW9 3AB

What is a rain forest?

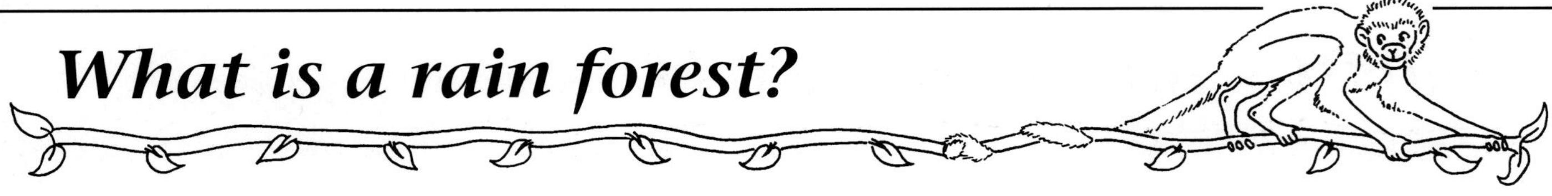

Name .... **Date** ....

Rain forests are thick forests full of trees, often covering a huge area. The trees are very close together and very tall. Little light reaches the ground, so inside the forest it is dark.

Rain forests grow in parts of the world where there is lots of rain. Most are near the Equator, an imaginary line that runs around the centre of the Earth. In these tropical rain forests it is hot and humid all the year round. The biggest is the Amazon rain forest, in South America.

Rain forests contain the richest variety of wildlife to be found anywhere on Earth. They are home to millions of different kinds of plants and animals. On every tree in the rain forest there may be over 100 different types of insects, plants and birds.

Rain forests are very important to everyone in the world. They provide us with timber, food, medicine and many other useful things. They also help to control the world's climate.

Write the correct answers to these questions.

1. Rain forests can be found near the .... (North Pole, Equator, Swiss Alps)

2. Rain forests are .... (wet, cold, windy)

3. Most of the trees are .... (short, tall, wide)

4. Rainforest trees are .... (wide apart, very small, close together)

5. Inside a rain forest it is .... (icy, dark, light)

6. Humid means .... (dry, snowy, warm and damp)

7. Rain forests are full of .... and ....
(factories, plants, people, animals)

8. Which is the largest area of rain forest in the world? Where is it?

....

9. Why are rain forests so important to us?

....

....

Where are the rain forests?

Name .... **Date** ....

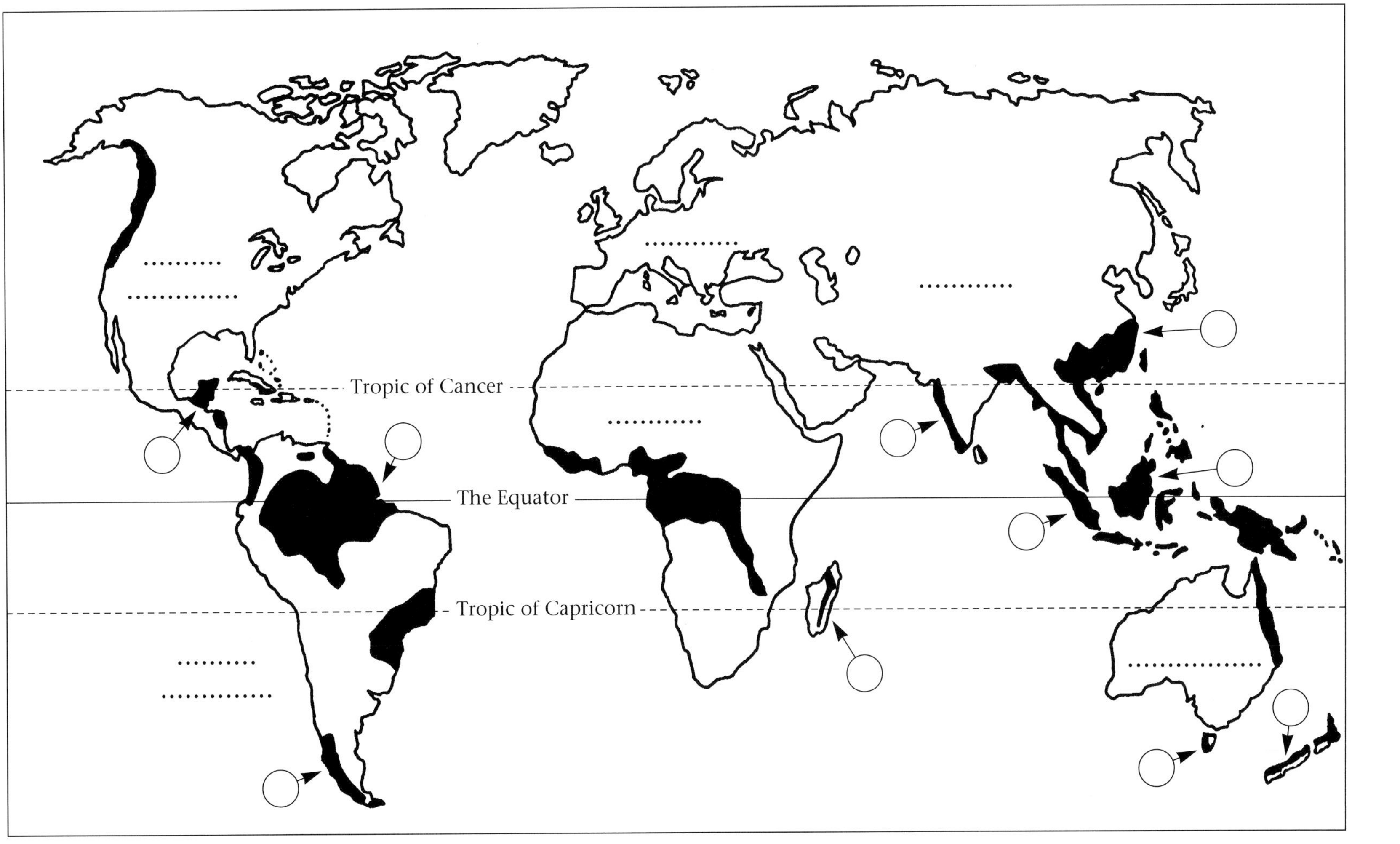

The black areas on the map show where the world's rain forests grow.

The tropical rain forests grow between the Tropics of Cancer and Capricorn. The temperate rain forests grow north and south of the tropics, where the rainfall is just as high but the temperature is lower.

Using an atlas to help you, find the places listed:

Name the continents on the map.

AFRICA
ASIA
NORTH AMERICA
AUSTRALASIA
EUROPE
SOUTH AMERICA

Write the numbers of the following countries in the correct circles.

1. Borneo
2. Brazil
3. Chile
4. China
5. India
6. Madagascar
7. Mexico
8. New Zealand
9. Sumatra
10. Tasmania

Tropical island

Name .... **Date** ....

This map shows the little island of St Lucia. It lies between the Equator and the Tropic of Cancer. One-tenth of the island is covered in dense rain forest.

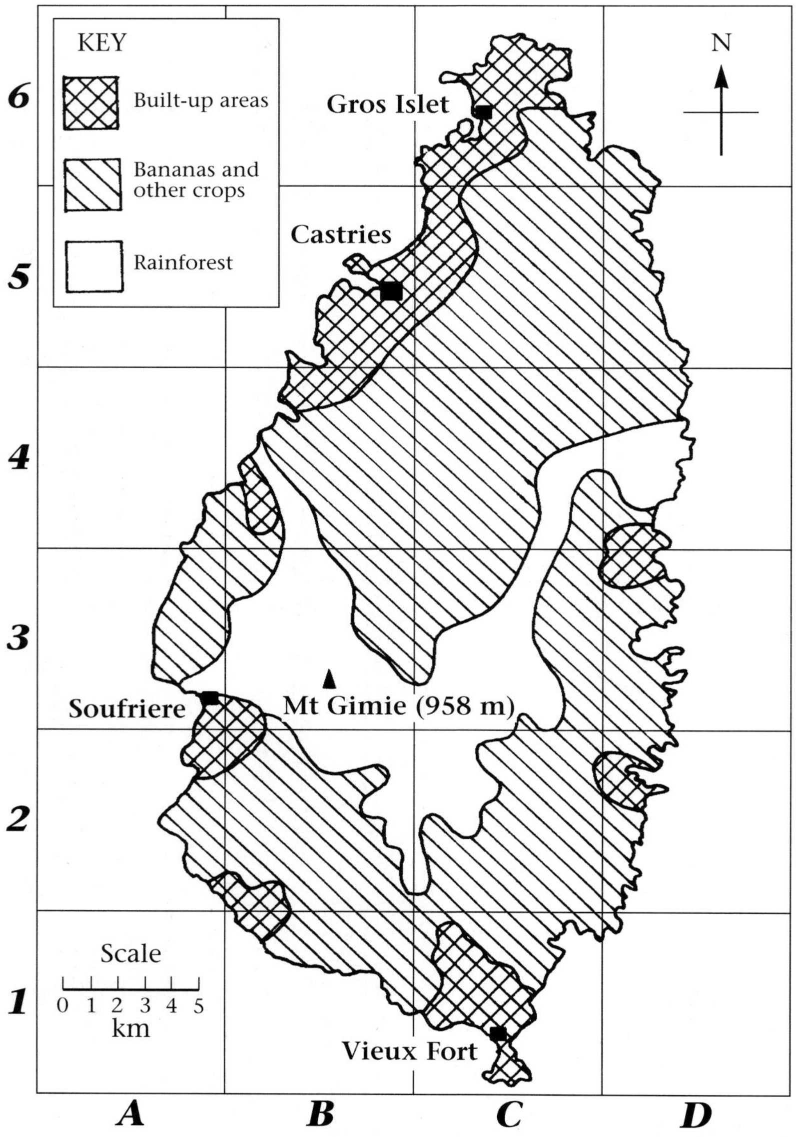

KEY
Built-up areas
Bananas and other crops
Rainforest

N

Gros Islet
Castries
Soufriere
Mt Gimie (958 m)
Vieux Fort

Scale
0 1 2 3 4 5
km

6 5 4 3 2 1
A B C D

1. Find St Lucia in an atlas.

a. Which is the nearest continent to St Lucia?

....

b. Which sea surrounds St Lucia?

....

c. To which group of islands does St Lucia belong?

....

2. On the map, add the other three points of the compass.

3. Use compass directions to describe where on St Lucia the following places can be found:

a. Soufriere is to the ....

b. Vieux Fort is to the ....

c. Gros Islet is to the ....

4. This map has a grid. Castries, the capital of St Lucia, is in square B5. Use the co-ordinates to describe exactly where to find:

a. Vieux Fort ....
b. Mt Gimie ....
c. Soufriere ....
d. Gros Islet ....

e. In which squares can you find areas of rain forest?

....

What's the weather like?

Name .... **Date** ....

Tropical rain forests have a very hot, humid climate. Temperatures range between 20–28° C all year round. The annual rainfall is between 1,500 and 4,000 mm. Afternoon thunderstorms are very common. There is no frost or drought, and there are no seasonal changes.

St Lucia

The temperature in St Lucia is about 27–28° C all year round. Rain falls throughout the year in short, heavy downpours. But the sun soon comes out again and quickly dries everything out.

These block graphs show the average monthly rainfall in London and in Vieux Fort, St Lucia. Compare the graphs and answer the following questions:

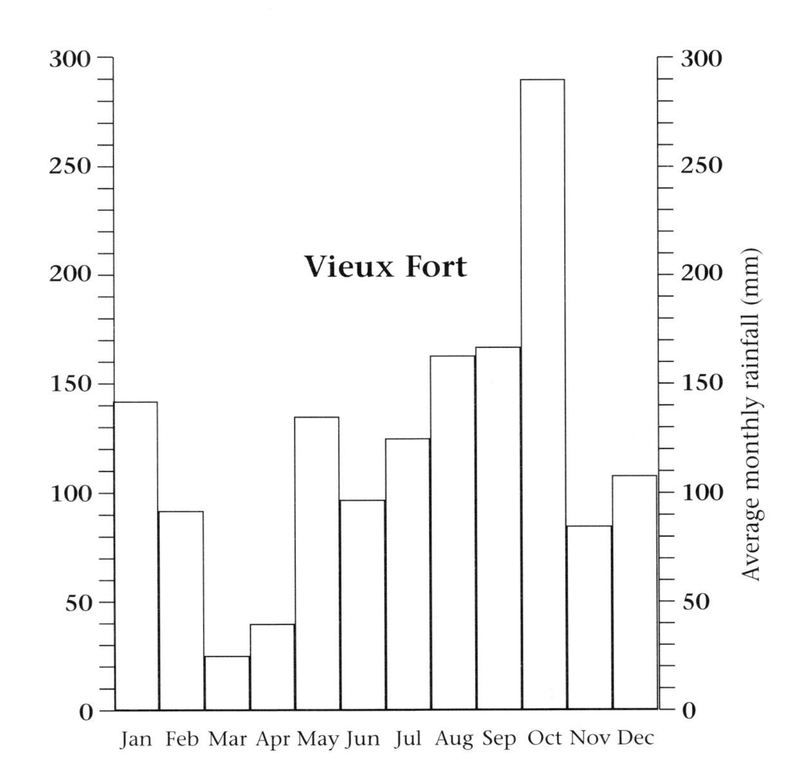

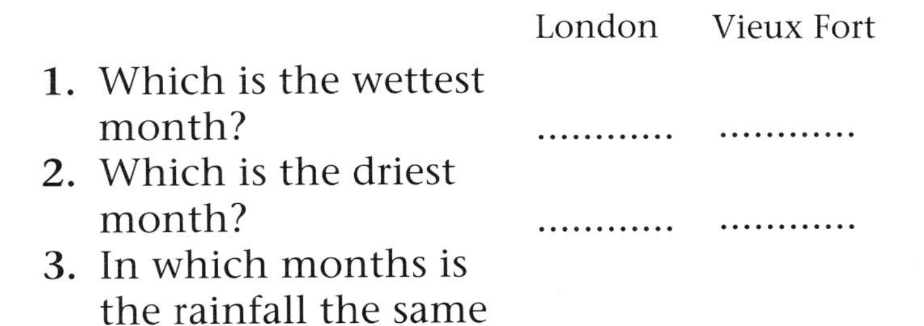

	London	Vieux Fort
1. Which is the wettest month?	....	....
2. Which is the driest month?	....	....
3. In which months is the rainfall the same in both places?	....	....

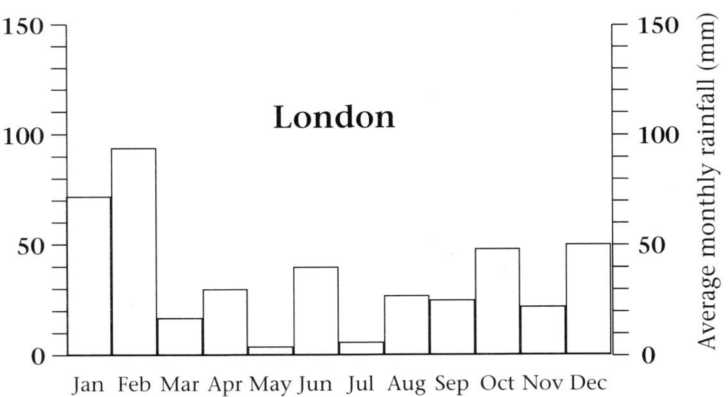

It is wetter in the rain forest in St Lucia than at Vieux Fort on the coast. Using the information below make a block graph, like those above, to show the average monthly rainfall in the rain forest.

Rain forest, St Lucia: average monthly rainfall (mm)

Jan	Feb	Mar	Apr	May	Jun	Jul	Aug	Sep	Oct	Nov	Dec
254	277	109	120	157	180	208	239	385	533	131	126

The water cycle

Name .... **Date** ....

Most rain forests grow in the hottest and wettest parts of the world. During the day, clouds gather over the forests. These clouds are full of water. Where do you think this water comes from?

Every drop of water on Earth has been used over and over again since time began. This natural recycling system is called the water cycle.

Look at the diagram. The numbers show the stages of the water cycle.

Now look at the six sentences below. They explain the stages of the water cycle, but they are not in the right order. Match the sentences to the six stages. Write the correct number next to each sentence.

☐ Rain-water is taken up by the forest plants, or flows into rivers and back to the sea.

☐ The water vapour rises, carried upwards by warm air.

☐ The water droplets get bigger and heavier and fall as rain.

☐ As it rises, the water vapour begins to cool down and forms clouds.

☐ The sun heats the water in the sea, rivers and forests, turning some of it into water vapour.

☐ Water droplets form in the clouds.

Write the meaning of the word **evaporation** in your glossary.

Rainforest layers

Name .... **Date** ....

The diagram shows the different layers of the rain forest. Can you name them, using the words below?

1. emergent trees ....
2. ....
3. ....
4. ....

(understorey, forest floor, ~~emergent trees,~~ canopy)

In which layer of the rain forest do the following live?

a. Fungi like dark, damp places and rotting wood.

....

b. Monkeys are at home among the dense tree tops.

....

c. Eagles build large nests in the tops of the highest trees.

....

d. Coral snakes live under logs or stones.

....

e. The tamandua is a tree-climbing anteater. It uses its tail to help it climb above the forest floor.

....

What's the difference?

Name .... **Date** ....

Tropical rain forests
Tropical rain forests are found in a belt around the Equator, where temperatures and rainfall are very high all year round. Most tropical rain forests are evergreen. There is very little change between the seasons, so the trees produce new leaves throughout the year.

Mangrove swamps are a special type of tropical rain forest. They line one-quarter of the world's tropical coastlines. Mangrove trees have long, stilt-like roots that lift the trunk above the mud and salty water.

Temperate rain forests
Most temperate rain forests grow along coasts. They are found near oceans in mountainous regions, to the north and south of the Tropics of Cancer and Capricorn. As they are further from the Equator, plant growth is affected by seasonal changes. Most plant growth happens in spring and summer when the weather is warmer. As well as evergreens there are deciduous trees, which shed their leaves in autumn.

Temperate rain forests contain many conifers. Some of these are the biggest and oldest trees on Earth. The largest area of temperate rain forest is on the west coast of North America. It stretches as far north as Alaska. Here there are giant redwoods which reach a height of 90 m, and bristlecone pines which are nearly 5,000 years old.

* *

Now you know some of the differences between tropical and temperate rain forests, can you answer these questions? Put a tick under the correct heading.

Which kind of rain forest ...

	Tropical	Temperate
1. ... has mostly evergreen trees?	....	....
2. ... is found in Alaska, North America?	....	....
3. ... contains mangrove trees?	....	....
4. ... has warmer weather in spring and summer?	....	....
5. ... has both evergreen and deciduous trees?	....	....
6. ... contains bristlecone pines?	....	....
7. ... is found near the Equator?	....	....
8. ... has few seasonal changes?	....	....
9. ... contains many conifers?	....	....
10. ... has high temperatures all year round?	....	....

Write the meanings of the words **deciduous**, **evergreen**, **temperate** and **tropical** in your glossary.

Decaying leaves

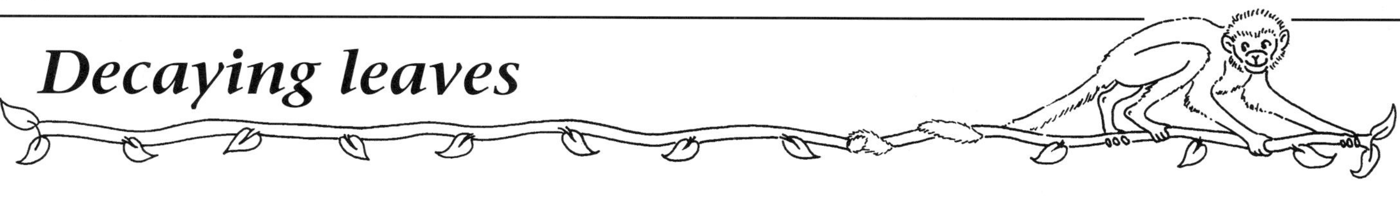

Name ....   **Date** ....

When leaves fall from the trees to the forest floor they begin to rot away. They are broken down by millions of tiny creatures, such as worms, insects and bacteria, which feed on dead plant and animal material. This process is known as decomposition.

As the dead material rots away, it produces mineral salts. These dissolve in water and pass into the soil. This enriches the soil, which feeds new plants and helps the trees to grow. As they grow, more leaves are produced. They later fall to the ground and rot away, and the cycle begins again.

Because it is hot and humid in the tropical rain forests, death, decay, new life and growth take place very quickly.

When rain forests are cut down, this cycle can no longer happen and the soil soon loses its goodness.

Complete these sentences:

1. The process of leaves rotting away is called ....
2. The leaves are eaten by ....
3. The broken down material is turned into ....
4. The process happens quickly in tropical rain forests because it is ....
5. Mineral salts are used by trees and plants as ....

Look at the picture on the left and describe, in your own words, what is happening.

....

....

....

....

....

Write the meaning of the word **decomposition** in your glossary.

Tropical tastes

Name .... **Date** ....

You can find these rainforest fruits in most large supermarkets. Label each fruit, using words from the list below.

① ....

② ....

③ ....

④ ....

⑤ ....

⑥ ....

⑦ ....

(starfruit, mango, avocado, bananas, lychees, pineapple, papaya)

* *

Rainforest recipe

Design a recipe card for a delicious rainforest ice-cream sundae.

Here are the ingredients:

- 2 scoops of vanilla ice cream
- 2 pieces of fruit (name your favourites)
- a teaspoonful of cocoa powder
- crushed Brazil nuts

On the card you will need to:

- list the ingredients
- write out the instructions
- draw pictures to illustrate your recipe
- think of an exotic name for the recipe

The instructions below are mixed up. You will need to put them in the correct order and number them.

- Cover with 2 scoops of ice cream.
- Slice up the fruit.
- Put the fruit into the bottom of a glass.
- Wash or peel the fruit.
- Sprinkle on the crushed nuts and cocoa.

Rainforest resources

Name ....   **Date** ....

Rainforest plants provide us with a great range of useful products, such as timber and different kinds of food. Some of the plants are used to make medicines.

One of the most valuable rainforest resources is rubber, which comes from the rubber tree. People who collect rubber are called rubber tappers. They make deep cuts in the tree trunks which ooze a thick white sap. The sap is collected in cups. Then it is mixed with water and acid, which turns it into solid rubber. Rubber tappers sell the rubber to factories, where it is made into other goods.

Circle the things below that are made from rubber:

car tyres	Wellington boots	hot water bottles
skateboard wheels	chewing gum	elastic bands
books	balloons	washing-up gloves

Can you think of two more?

....

Look at the products below. Which rainforest plants do they come from? Using a coloured pencil, join each product to its correct information box.

1.

2.

3.

4.

A.	B.	C.	D.
made from the beans of the cacao tree	made from the sap of the sapodilla tree	made from the nuts of the kola tree	made from the beans of the coffee tree

Monkey puzzle

Name .... **Date** ....

Many kinds of monkey live in the tropical rain forests. Here are four of them. Follow the trails to find out where each monkey lives.

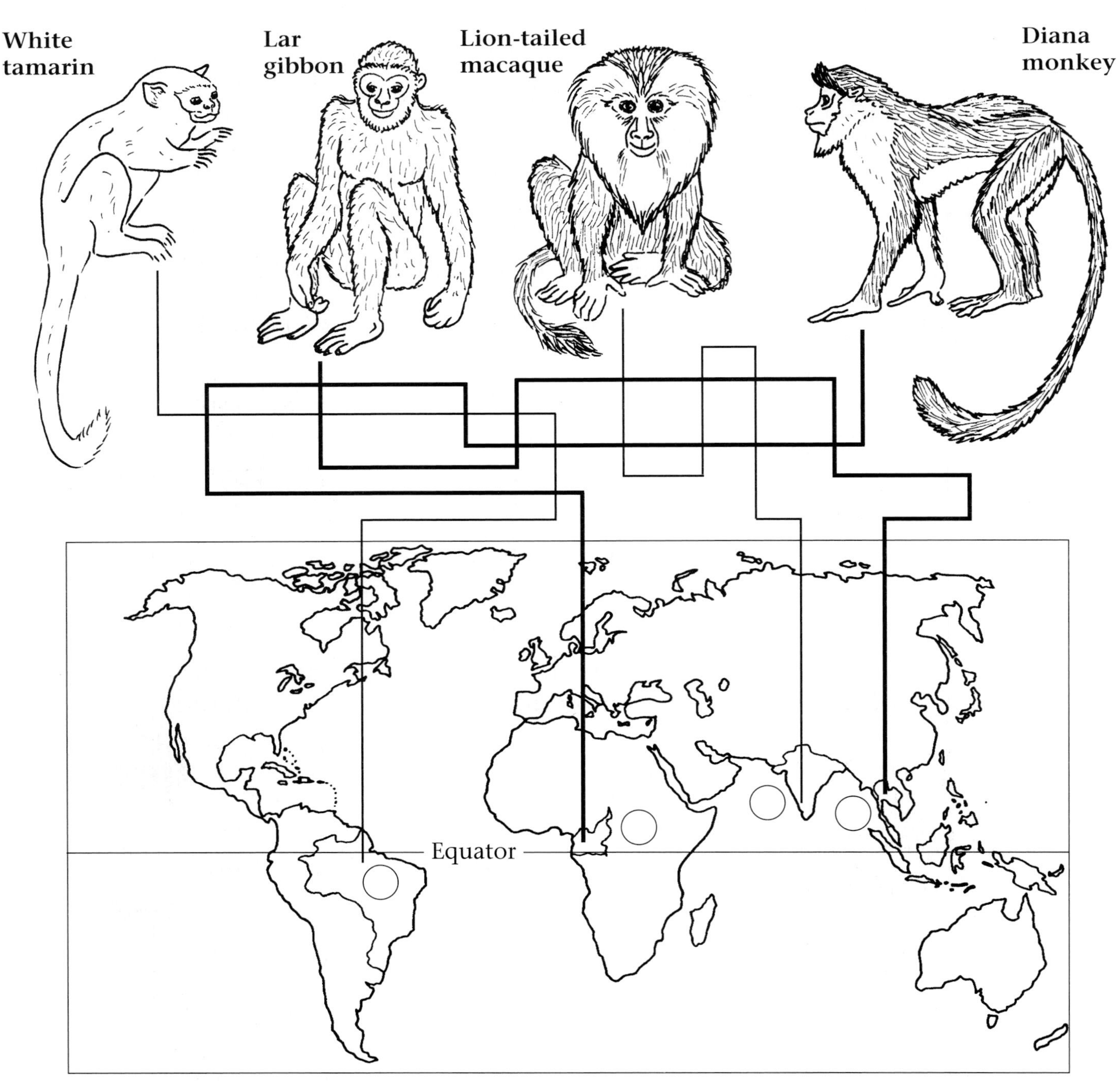

① **Cameroon** ② **Brazil** ③ **Thailand** ④ **India**

Use an atlas to help you identify the four countries above.
Write the number of the country in its correct circle on the map.

Butterfly patterns

Name .... **Date** ....

Many of the world's largest butterflies can be found in rain forests. Some are brightly coloured. Others are camouflaged to look like leaves. This means it is hard for them to be seen by predators, such as birds.

Complete the butterfly drawings below. Each side is symmetrical, which means that the shape, size and colour of the wings are the same on each side of the body.

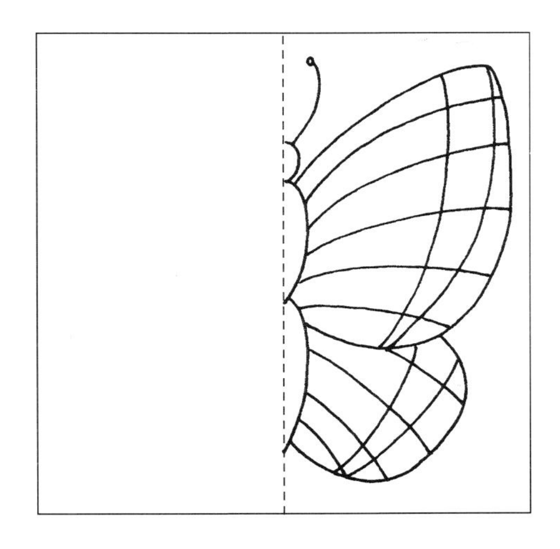

When you have finished your drawings, colour them in. Make two of them brightly coloured, and two of them camouflaged to look like leaves.

What's down there?

Name .... **Date** ....

The forest floor teems with millions of insects and tiny creatures. Here are just four of them. Complete the sentences below, using words from the bottom of each box.

Leaf-cutting ants

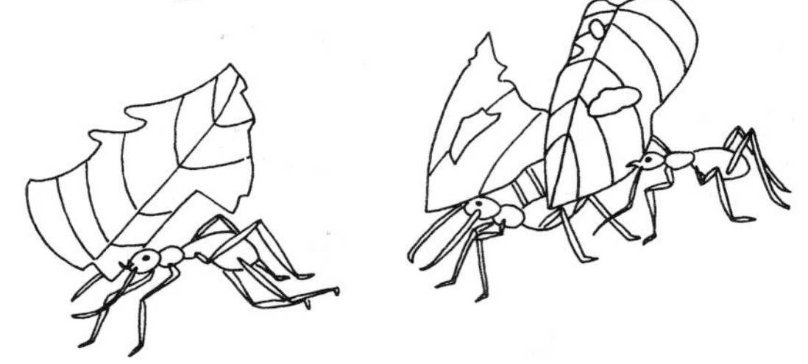

Leaf-cutting ants live on the .... floor. They use their sharp jaws to cut up pieces of .... They make tiny piles of .... from the leaves. They feed on the .... which grow on this compost.

(leaf, fungi, compost, forest)

Centipede

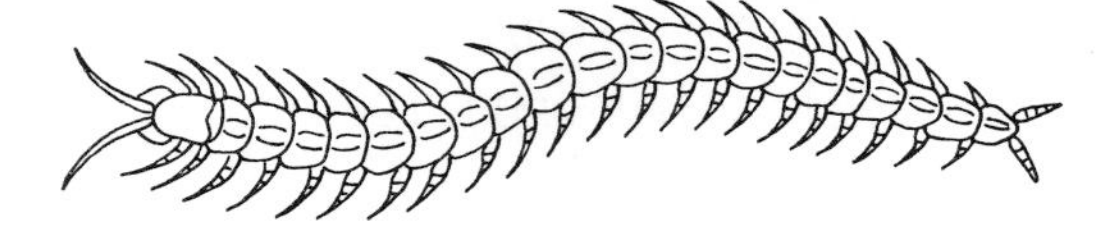

Centipedes are fierce .... They eat other small creatures. Their .... are laid in soil. When the young hatch they look just like the .... They have one pair of .... on each segment of their long thin body.

(eggs, legs, predators, adults)

Bird-eating spider

Bird-eating spiders live under .... and in .... They eat small .... They kill their prey with .... from their jaws.

(holes, poison, logs, birds)

Scorpion

Scorpions have a sting at the end of their .... It is used to protect them from predators. The .... is also used to .... small animals, which the scorpion then eats. Scorpions hunt at ....

(kill, night, sting, tail)

Write the meanings of the words **predator** and **prey** in your glossary.

Which of the creatures above is not a predator? ....

River reptiles

Name .... **Date** ....

Crocodiles are ferocious predators that lurk in rainforest rivers, but there is more to them than that!

Look at all the adjectives below and circle which ones you think best describe crocodiles.

Add some of your own.

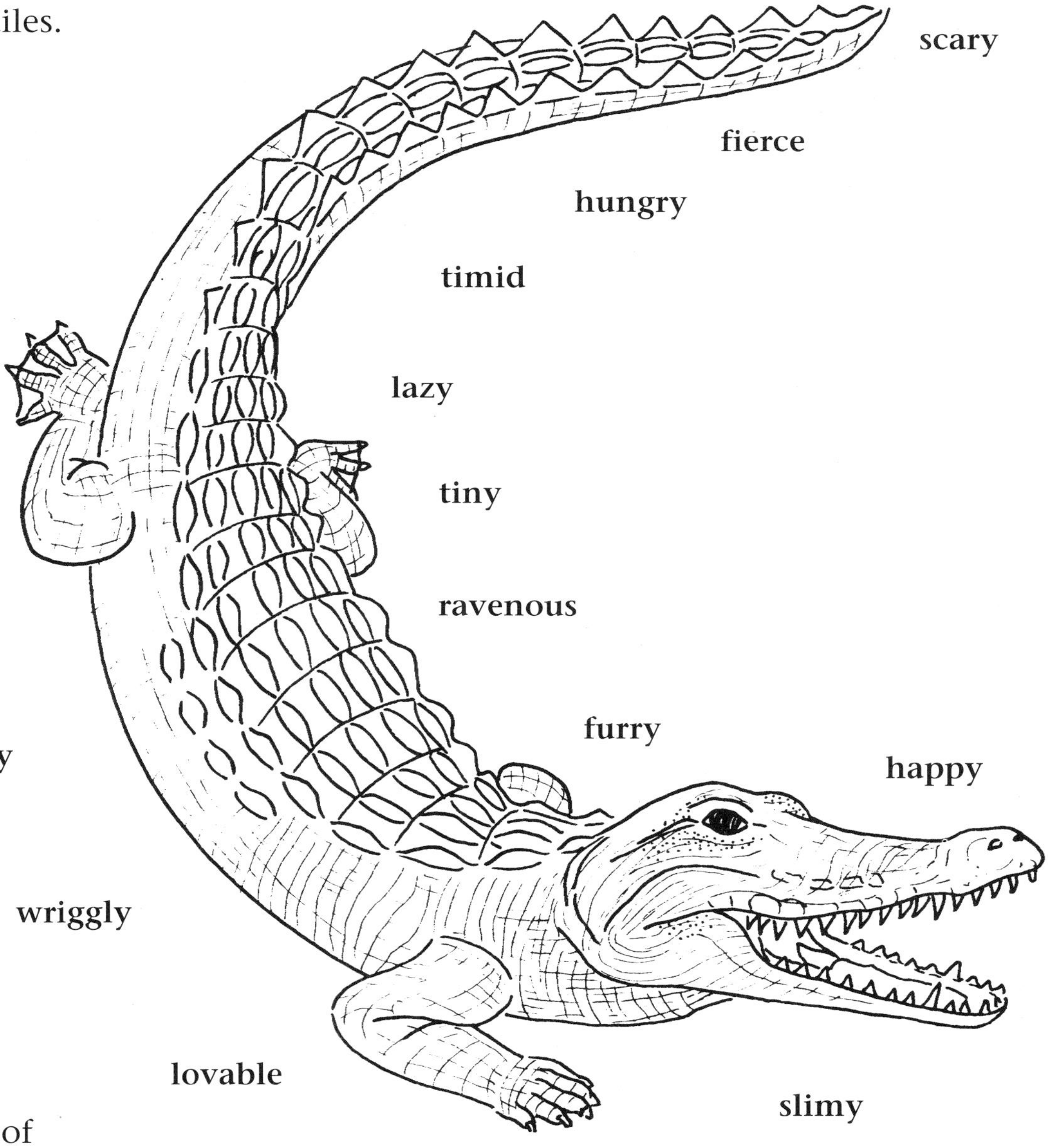

scary

fierce

hungry

timid

lazy

tiny

cuddly

ravenous

furry

scaly

happy

wriggly

lovable

slimy

On a separate sheet of paper, use some of the adjectives above to write a poem about a crocodile.

Write the meaning of the word **reptile** in your glossary.

Birds and beaks

Name .... **Date** ....

Over 2,500 different kinds of birds live in the tropical rain forests. They come in all shapes, sizes and colours. Their beaks come in different shapes and sizes, too. This is because their beaks are adapted to help them eat the food they need.

Look at the birds below and then answer the questions.

The **scarlet macaw** is the largest parrot in South America. Its beak has sharp edges which work like nutcrackers.

The **harpy eagle** soars high above the rain forest. It preys on small animals in the canopy below.

The little **hummingbird** darts among the rain forest flowers.

The **toucan** has one of the biggest beaks of any bird. This helps it to reach out for food on little twigs.

The **skimmer** lives near water and catches its food as it flies. The lower part of its beak is longer than the top part.

1. Which bird has a long thin beak for collecting flower nectar and tiny insects?
2. Which bird has a hooked beak for tearing apart its prey?
3. Which bird has a strong beak and eats Brazil nuts?
4. Which bird has a very big beak for picking fruit?
5. Which bird ploughs part of its beak through water to scoop up fish?

Rainforest mammals

Name .... **Date** ....

Fill in the sentences below using the information provided.
Then, on a separate sheet of paper, answer the questions that follow.

The three-toed sloth

The sloth lives in ....
It is camouflaged among the forest trees by ....
....
It clings to trees using its ....
....
It moves slowly, but spends most of its day completely ....
It is more active ....

slow moving

long hook-like claws

found in South America

tiny green algae live on its fur

nocturnal

clings to tree trunks or hangs upside-down from branches

may stay in same tree for years

spends up to 18 hours a day not moving

The orang-utan

The orang-utan is found in ....
.... where it is known as... .
Orang-utans swing hand-over-hand through the trees using their
....
At night they sleep on ....
....

builds own sleeping platform of twigs in the fork of a tree

long, shaggy reddish-brown hair

lives in Borneo and Sumatra in Malaysia

long, powerful arms which reach down to its ankles

swings rapidly through trees

name means 'man of the forest' in Malay language

1. List the similarities between sloths and orang-utans.
2. List the differences.
3. How is each animal adapted to life in the rain forest?
4. Write the meanings of the words **mammal** and **nocturnal** in your glossary.

Food chains

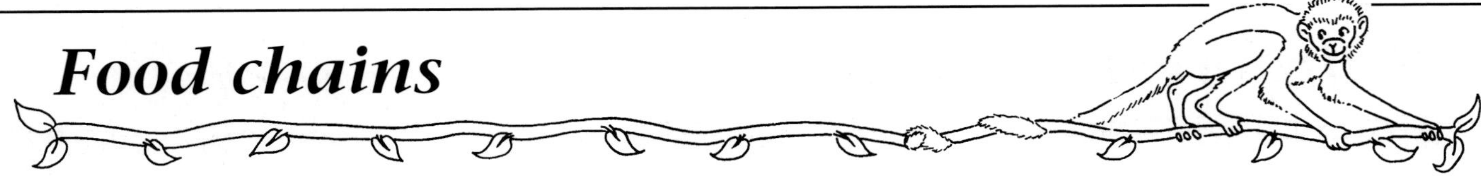

Name .... **Date** ....

A food chain is the feeding link between plants and animals. Most food chains begin with green plants, which use the sun's energy to make food in their leaves. This energy is passed on to the animal that eats the plant, and is passed on again when that animal is eaten by another.

In the rain forest, the food chain links the smallest and simplest plants to carnivorous animals such as piranha fish, anacondas and tigers. There are many food chains, which all link together to form a food web.

Look at the four food chains shown here and see if you can complete them. Choose from the answers below.

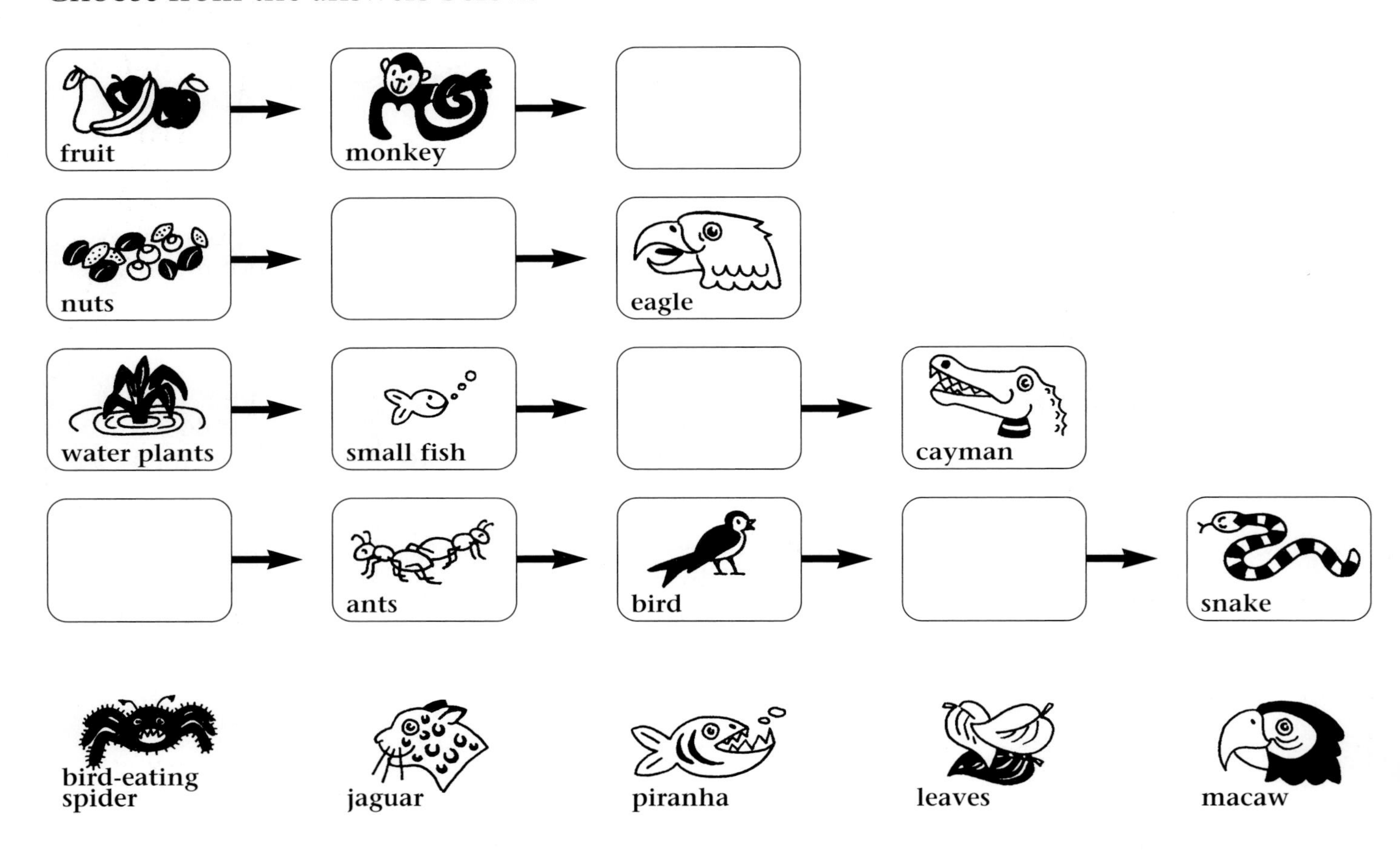

Now make up your own example of a simple food chain, ending with yourself.

Write the meanings of the following words in your glossary:
carnivore, herbivore, omnivore.

Rainforest dreams

Name .... **Date** ....

Finish this story:

They were woken during the night by the rainforest noises. Beyond the clearing, leaves rustled and branches snapped as animals moved through the forest around them. Water dripped from the trees, frogs croaked, parrots squawked and monkeys screeched. Suddenly the front flaps of their tent moved apart and there in the bright moonlight stood ...

....

....

....

What happened next?

....

....

....

....

....

....

....

....

....

....

....

....

....

....

....

Draw and colour a picture to illustrate your story.

Top cats

Name .... Date ....

The wild cats that live in the rain forests are fierce predators. They kill and eat animals and fish. Their coats are often camouflaged by spots or stripes. This helps them blend in with the light and shadows of the rainforest trees as they stalk their prey. They move quickly and are excellent at climbing and swimming.

The jaguar has a spotted coat and is the largest wild cat in South America. The tiger has a stripy coat and is the biggest cat in the world. It lives mainly in India and South-east Asia.

Jaguars and tigers are now endangered animals. Early in this century they were hunted for sport. Farmers killed them to protect their cattle. Over the last fifty years, great areas of rain forest have been cut down to clear land for farming, logging, mining and housing. This means there are fewer places left for the wild cats to live. They are also hunted for their beautiful skins.

Jaguars are now protected by law but they are still hunted and trapped by poachers. In 1900 there were about 100,000 tigers in the world, but now there are fewer than 7,500. Half of these live in India. Although 80 per cent of India's tigers are in areas of land protected by law, their numbers are still going down. Conservation groups such as the World Wide Fund for Nature (WWF) are doing all they can to protect these animals, but some people think the tigers of India will be extinct by the year 2010.

Answer the following questions using full sentences.

1. Name two types of cat that can be found in rain forests.
2. Which of these cats is the biggest?
3. Why are their coats camouflaged?
4. Which cat is now protected by law?
5. How many tigers are there left in India? Is the number increasing or decreasing?
6. Give two reasons why the cats of the rain forests are still dropping in numbers.
7. What is being done to protect these animals?
8. Do you think it is wrong to kill animals for their fur? Give reasons for your answer.
9. Compose a letter to the World Wide Fund for Nature, asking for information about its work with endangered animals.
10. Write the meanings of the following words in your glossary: **endangered, extinct.**

Antonio lives in the rain forest

Name .... **Date** ....

"My name is Antonio José and I live in the rain forest, in Brazil. My father is a rubber tapper. He collects the white sap from the wild rubber trees that grow in the forest around here, near the Armadillo River, and I help him.

"I have got one little brother, Chico, who's just six months old, and two sisters: Maria Aparecida who's five and Maria Nazare who's three. Because I'm the oldest I help my mother with little Chico. Because our house is raised up off the ground we have to make sure Chico doesn't fall out. He did once because our black pigs trotted out from under the house and started snuffling round him.

"We use the forest to get nearly everything we need. We grow nearly all our food in two gardens in the forest. Our houses are built from three different sorts of palm: we use the wood from one for the floor, and the bark from another for the walls. Our thatched roof is made from the great big leaf fronds of palm trees.

"My best friend Raimundo lives just down the path, but we don't get much time to play because we're usually helping with chores around the house. Both of us help look after our brothers and sisters, and I help dad collecting rubber too. We don't have many toys, but sometimes we borrow the wooden aeroplane that my friend Jose's dad made.

"I don't know what a school is like. Neither do my mum or dad. Nobody from here in Mato Grosso has ever been to one. Dad says schools are very important because they teach you lots of useful things."

Antonio has never been out of the rain forest.
He doesn't know how different life is here.

Write a letter to Antonio. Tell him all about your family and friends, where you live and what you like to do. Tell him what it is like to go to school.

Rainforest trek – 1

Name .... **Date** ....

You and your friends have planned a trek through the rain forest to search for a lost temple. Which of you will find it first? To begin, each player throws the dice once. The trekker with the highest score sets off first. Take care – it's dangerous deep in the rain forest!

Rainforest trek – 2

Name .... **Date** ....

What did you come across on your rainforest trek?
Would any of the items below have been useful?
Tick ten things from the list below.
Give your reasons for choosing them.

- ☐ tape recorder ....
- ☐ map ....
- ☐ compass ....
- ☐ knife ....
- ☐ insect spray ....
- ☐ water bottle ....
- ☐ camera ....
- ☐ magnifying glass ....
- ☐ radio ....
- ☐ boots ....
- ☐ scissors ....
- ☐ hat ....
- ☐ mosquito net ....
- ☐ notebook ....
- ☐ sun-glasses ....
- ☐ torch ....
- ☐ a set of plastic containers .....
- ☐ gloves ....

On your next trek you plan to take a bigger rucksack. It will have room for two more items not on this list. What will you take and why?

....
....
....

Deforestation

Name .... **Date** ....

People have lived in rain forests for thousands of years. They live in harmony with the forest, scattered in small villages which are built on cleared land. But around the world the population is increasing at a great rate. This has two effects on the rain forests. More rainforest products are wanted. Land is needed to make room for more houses, farms and roads.

Every day huge areas of forest are cut or burnt down. This clearing away of forests is called deforestation. In the last 50 years half the world's rain forests have disappeared. By the year 2010 there may only be tiny areas of rain forest left. With nowhere to live, many of the world's rarest animals will become extinct. Rainforest peoples will lose their hunting grounds and homes. Scientists are also worried that if too many trees are chopped down our climate will start to change.

All over the world, people are trying to halt the destruction of the forests so that they can be saved for the future.

Circle the correct answers:

1. Large areas of the rainforest are being cleared. True / False

2. Fire kills plants and animals in the forest. True / False

3. Some animals have nowhere to go if the forest is cut down. True / False

4. People do not lose their homes when the forest is destroyed. True / False

5. There will only be small areas of rain forest left by the year 2010. True / False

Now answer these questions:

6. Why are rain forests being cut down?

7. How does deforestation affect rainforest peoples?

8. How does deforestation affect rainforest wildlife?

Write the meaning of the word **deforestation** in your glossary.

Down it comes

Name ....

Date ....

You live in a village near the edge of the rain forest. One day each villager receives this letter.

Choppem Down Logging Company
Boa Vista
Brazil

23 March

Dear Villager

We are writing to inform you that we will be cutting down the trees around your village next month, as we need to sell more timber. The tractors and bulldozers will arrive on Monday.

Yours faithfully

Miguel Cortez

Miguel Cortez
Manager

In small groups discuss how this will affect you and your village.

Write a letter to the company manager saying why the trees should stay.

When you write your letter:
- Be neat.
- Be polite.
- Give your reasons clearly.

Glossary

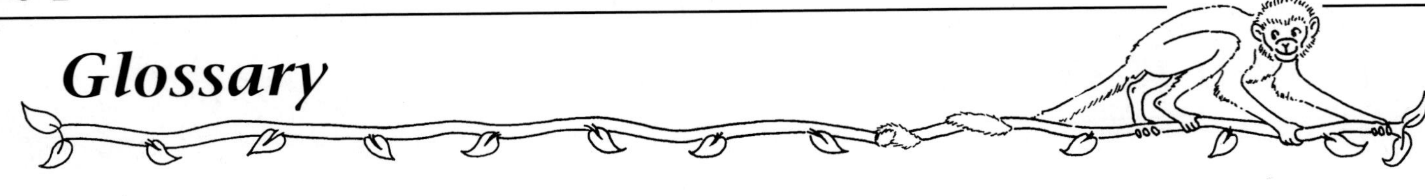

Name .... **Date** ....

The worksheets contain words which may be new to you. Some of them are listed below. Write the meaning next to the word in as much detail as possible. The first one has been done for you, as an example. If you are not sure of the meaning, use a dictionary to help you.

camouflage The colours or markings on an animal which make it look like its surroundings, so that it cannot be easily seen.

carnivore ....

....

deciduous ....

....

decomposition ....

....

....

deforestation ....

....

....

endangered ....

....

evaporation ....

....

....

evergreen ....

....

extinct ....

....

herbivore ....

....

mammal ....

....

....

nocturnal ....

....

omnivore ....

....

predator ....

....

prey ....

....

reptile ....

....

....

temperate ....

....

....

tropical ....

....

....